Chorale Preludes for Manuals

Johann Sebastian Bach

Book Two

Kevin
Mayhew

Extracted from

The Complete Organ Works of J S Bach

Executive Editor   Alan Ridout
Managing Editor   Anthea Smith
Music Setting   Christopher Hinkins

This compilation first published in Great Britain in 1996 by
KEVIN MAYHEW LTD
Rattlesden
Bury St Edmunds
Suffolk IP30 0SZ

ISBN 0 86209 747 9
Catalogue No: 1400044

Printed and bound in Hong Kong

Contents

Ich hab' mein' Sach' Gott heimgestellt BWV 1113 — 6
I have entrusted my case to God

In dich hab' ich gehoffet, Herr BWV 712 — 8
I have put my hope in you, Lord

Jesu, meine Freude BWV 713 — 10
Jesus, my joy

Jesus Christus, unser Heiland BWV 689 — 14
Jesus Christ, our Saviour

Jesus, meine Zuversicht BWV 728 — 16
Jesus, my trust and my Saviour

Kyrie, Gott Heiliger Geist BWV 674 — 17
Lord God, Holy Spirit

Kyrie, Gott Vater in Ewigkeit BWV 672 — 18
Lord God, Eternal Father

Lob sei dem allmächtigen Gott BWV 704 — 19
Praise to Almighty God

Machs mit mir, Gott, nach deiner Güt BWV 957 — 20
Do with me, God, according to your goodness

Nun freut euch, lieben Christen g'mein BWV 734 — 22
All Christians now rejoice

Nun laßt uns den Leib begraben BWV 1111 — 24
Now let us bury the body

Nun komm, der Heiden Heiland BWV 699 — 26
Come now, Saviour of all

O Jesu, wie ist dein Gestalt BWV 1094 — 27
O Jesus, how deeply was your body wounded

O Herre Gott, dein göttlich Wort BWV 1110 — 28
Lord God, your divine word

O Lamm Gottes, unschuldig BWV 1095 — 30
O Lamb of God, innocently put to death

O Lamm Gottes, unschuldig (No BWV reference) — 32
O Lamb of God, innocently put to death

Vater unser im Himmelreich BWV 683 — 34
Our Father in heaven

Vater unser im Himmelreich BWV 737 — 35
Our Father in heaven

Vom Himmel hoch, da komm' ich her BWV 701 — 36
From highest heaven I come, bringing good tidings

Was Gott tut, das ist wohlgetan BWV 1116 — 38
Whatever God does is done well

Wenn dich Unglück tut greifen an BWV 1104 — 39
If disaster befalls and misfortune has its way

Wer nur den lieben Gott läßt walten BWV 690 — 40
He who lets dear God guide him

Wer nur den lieben Gott läßt walten BWV 691 — 41
He who lets dear God guide him

Werde munter, mein Gumüte BWV 1118 — 42
Awake, my feelings and my senses

Wie nach einer Wasserquelle BWV 1119 — 43
Be joyful, O my soul

Wir Christenleut' BWV 1090 — 44
Christians now rejoice

Wir glauben all' an einen Gott BWV 1098 — 46
We all believe in one God

Wir glauben all' an einen Gott BWV 681 — 48
We all believe in one God

Ornamentation

J S Bach himself left one indicator on ornamentation in the form of a table of thirteen ornaments and their written-out equivalents for his ten-year-old son, Wilhelm Friedemann. It is given here without the brief verbal descriptions which in many cases are now either obsolete or actually misleading.

It is tempting to exaggerate the importance of this list coming, as it does, from the hand of the master and for an instructional purpose. There are problems to it as it is applied to specific music; and it is not comprehensive. Yet to focus too assiduously on the problems is probably to underestimate its importance. So long as it is taken as a general guide and not as an infallible statement it will prove very useful.

ALAN RIDOUT

'Explanation of various signs, showing how to play certain ornaments neatly'

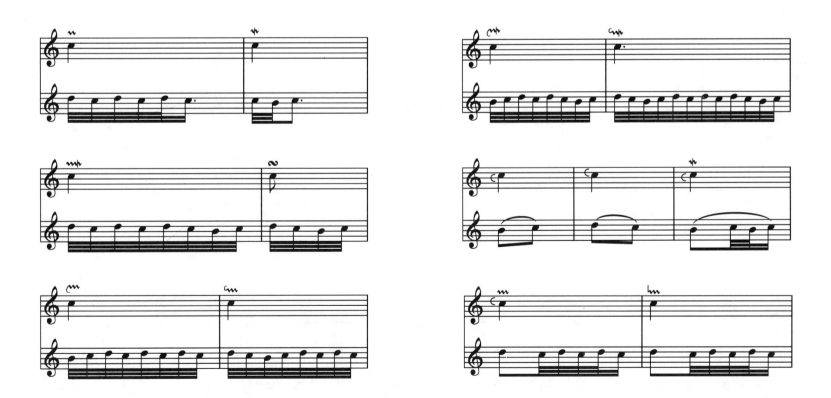

Ich hab' mein' Sach' Gott heimgestellt

BWV 1113

In dich hab' ich gehoffet, Herr

BWV 712
manualiter

Jesu, meine Freude

BWV 713
manualiter

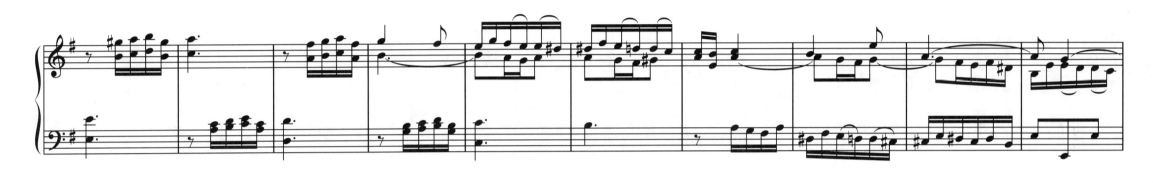

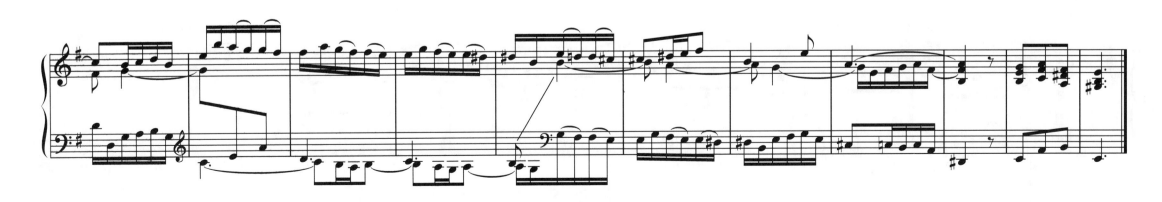

Jesus Christus, unser Heiland

BWV 689
manualiter
a 4

Jesus, meine Zuversicht

BWV 728
manualiter

Kyrie, Gott heiliger Geist

BWV 674

Kyrie, Gott Vater in Ewigkeit

BWV 672
manualiter
alio modo

Lob sei dem allmächtigen Gott

BWV 704
manualiter
fughetta

Machs mit mir, Gott, nach deiner Güt

BWV 957

Nun freut euch, lieben Christen g'mein
(Es ist gewißlich an der Zeit)

BWV 734
manualiter
choralis in tenore

Nun laßt uns den Leib begraben

BWV 1111

Nun komm, der Heiden Heiland

BWV 699
manualiter
fughetta

O Jesu, wie ist dein Gestalt

BWV 1094

O Herre Gott, dein göttlich Wort

BWV 1110

O Lamm Gottes, unschuldig

BWV 1095

O Lamm Gottes, unschuldig

(No BWV reference)

Vater unser im Himmelreich

BWV 683
manualiter
alio modo

Vater unser im Himmelreich

BWV 737
manualiter

This edition © Copyright 1994 Kevin Mayhew Ltd.

Vom Himmel hoch, da komm' ich her

BWV 701
manualiter
fughetta

Was Gott tut, das ist wohlgetan

BWV 1116

Wenn dich Unglück tut greifen an

BWV 1104

Wer nur den lieben Gott läßt walten

Wer nur den lieben Gott läßt walten

BWV 691
manualiter

Werde munter, mein Gumüte

BWV 1118

Wie nach einer Wasserquelle

BWV 1119

Wir Christenleut'

BWV 1090

Wir glauben all' an einen Gott

BWV 1098

Wir glauben all' an einen Gott

BWV 681
manualiter